This Book Belongs To:

____

____

____

Dedication

This Recipe Book is dedicated to all the mothers and daughters who want to preserve the family recipes and pass them along for generations to come.

You are my inspiration for producing this book and I'm honored to be a part of your recipe collection and organization.

How To Use this Book

This Recipe Book will help guide you by accurately recording each of your favorite family recipes and jotting down new ones throughout the upcoming years.

Here are examples of information for you to fill in and write the details of your recipe collection.

Fill in the following information:

1. Table of Contents for each recipe page
2. Recipe name
3. Servings, prep time, and cook time
4. Ingredients
5. Directions
6. From the kitchen of - place to write who the recipe is from
7. Notes

Table of Contents

Page #	Recipe Name

Table of Contents

Table of Contents

Page #	Recipe Name

Table of Contents

Table of Contents

Page #	Recipe Name

Table of Contents

Page #	Recipe Name

Recipe Name

Servings:__________ Prep Time:______________ Cook Time:__________

Ingredients:

Directions:

From The Kitchen Of:____________________

Notes

Recipe Name

Servings:__________Prep Time:______________Cook Time:__________

Ingredients:

Directions:

From The Kitchen Of:______________________________

Notes

Recipe Name

Servings:__________ Prep Time:_______________ Cook Time:___________

Ingredients:

Directions:

From The Kitchen Of:

Notes

Recipe Name

Servings:__________ Prep Time:__________ Cook Time:__________

Ingredients:

Directions:

From The Kitchen Of:__________

Notes

Recipe Name

Servings:__________ Prep Time:_______________ Cook Time:__________

Ingredients:

Directions:

From The Kitchen Of:

Notes

Recipe Name

Servings:__________ Prep Time:__________ Cook Time:__________

Ingredients:

Directions:

From The Kitchen Of:

Notes

Recipe Name

Servings:__________ Prep Time:__________ Cook Time:__________

Ingredients:

Directions:

From The Kitchen Of:__________

Notes

Recipe Name

Servings:__________ Prep Time:__________ Cook Time:__________

Ingredients:

Directions:

From The Kitchen Of:__________

Notes

Recipe Name

Servings:__________ Prep Time:__________ Cook Time:__________

Ingredients:

Directions:

From The Kitchen Of:__________

Notes

Recipe Name

Servings:__________ Prep Time:______________ Cook Time:__________

Ingredients:

Directions:

From The Kitchen Of:______________________________

Notes

Recipe Name

Servings:__________ Prep Time:_______________ Cook Time:__________

Ingredients:

Directions:

From The Kitchen Of:_______________

Notes

Recipe Name

Servings:__________ Prep Time:__________ Cook Time:__________

Ingredients:

Directions:

From The Kitchen Of:__________

Notes

Recipe Name

Servings:________ Prep Time:________ Cook Time:________

Ingredients:

Directions:

From The Kitchen Of:________

Notes

Recipe Name

Servings:__________ Prep Time:__________ Cook Time:__________

Ingredients:

Directions:

From The Kitchen Of:__________

Notes

Recipe Name

Servings:__________ Prep Time:______________ Cook Time:__________

Ingredients:

Directions:

From The Kitchen Of:______________________________

Notes

Recipe Name

Servings:__________ Prep Time:__________ Cook Time:__________

Ingredients:

Directions:

From The Kitchen Of:

Notes

Recipe Name

Servings:__________ Prep Time:______________ Cook Time:__________

Ingredients:

Directions:

From The Kitchen Of:

Notes

Recipe Name

Servings:__________ Prep Time:__________ Cook Time:__________

Ingredients:

Directions:

From The Kitchen Of:

Notes

Recipe Name

Servings:__________ Prep Time:_______________ Cook Time:__________

Ingredients:

Directions:

From The Kitchen Of:

Notes

Recipe Name

Servings:________ Prep Time:________ Cook Time:________

Ingredients:

Directions:

From The Kitchen Of:________

Notes

Recipe Name

Servings:__________ Prep Time:______________ Cook Time:__________

Ingredients:

Directions:

From The Kitchen Of:____________________

Notes

Recipe Name

Servings:__________ Prep Time:__________ Cook Time:__________

Ingredients:

Directions:

From The Kitchen Of:__________

Notes

Recipe Name

Servings:__________ Prep Time:______________ Cook Time:__________

Ingredients:

Directions:

From The Kitchen Of:____________________

Notes

Recipe Name

Servings:__________ Prep Time:__________ Cook Time:__________

Ingredients:

Directions:

From The Kitchen Of:__________

Notes

Recipe Name

Servings:__________ Prep Time:__________ Cook Time:__________

Ingredients:

Directions:

From The Kitchen Of:

Notes

Recipe Name

Servings:__________ Prep Time:__________ Cook Time:__________

Ingredients:

Directions:

From The Kitchen Of:

Notes

Recipe Name

Servings:__________ Prep Time:__________ Cook Time:__________

Ingredients:

Directions:

From The Kitchen Of:__________

Notes

Recipe Name

Servings:__________ Prep Time:__________ Cook Time:__________

Ingredients:

Directions:

From The Kitchen Of:__________

Notes

Recipe Name

Servings:__________ Prep Time:______________ Cook Time:__________

Ingredients:

Directions:

From The Kitchen Of:____________________

Notes

Recipe Name

Servings:__________ Prep Time:__________ Cook Time:__________

Ingredients:

Directions:

From The Kitchen Of:__________

Notes

Recipe Name

Servings:________ Prep Time:________ Cook Time:________

Ingredients:

Directions:

From The Kitchen Of:________

Notes

Recipe Name

Servings:__________ Prep Time:__________ Cook Time:__________

Ingredients:

Directions:

From The Kitchen Of:

Notes

Recipe Name

Servings:__________ Prep Time:__________ Cook Time:__________

Ingredients:

Directions:

From The Kitchen Of:__________

Notes

Recipe Name

Servings:__________ Prep Time:__________ Cook Time:__________

Ingredients:

Directions:

From The Kitchen Of:

Notes

Recipe Name

Servings:__________ Prep Time:__________ Cook Time:__________

Ingredients:

Directions:

From The Kitchen Of:__________

Notes

Recipe Name

Servings:__________ Prep Time:__________ Cook Time:__________

Ingredients:

Directions:

From The Kitchen Of:__________

Notes

Recipe Name

Servings:__________ Prep Time:______________ Cook Time:__________

Ingredients:

Directions:

From The Kitchen Of:

Notes

Recipe Name

Servings:__________ Prep Time:__________ Cook Time:__________

Ingredients:

Directions:

From The Kitchen Of:__________

Notes

Recipe Name

Servings:__________ Prep Time:______________ Cook Time:__________

Ingredients:

Directions:

From The Kitchen Of:______________________________

Notes

Recipe Name

Servings:__________ Prep Time:__________ Cook Time:__________

Ingredients:

Directions:

From The Kitchen Of:__________

Notes

Recipe Name

Servings:__________Prep Time:_______________Cook Time:__________

Ingredients:

Directions:

From The Kitchen Of:______________________________

Notes

Recipe Name

Servings:__________ Prep Time:______________ Cook Time:__________

Ingredients:

Directions:

From The Kitchen Of:

Notes

Recipe Name

Servings:__________Prep Time:______________Cook Time:__________

Ingredients:

Directions:

From The Kitchen Of:____________________________

Notes

Recipe Name

Servings:__________Prep Time:______________Cook Time:__________

Ingredients:

Directions:

From The Kitchen Of:

Notes

Recipe Name

Servings:__________ Prep Time:______________ Cook Time:__________

Ingredients:

Directions:

From The Kitchen Of:______________________________

Notes

Recipe Name

Servings:__________ Prep Time:______________ Cook Time:__________

Ingredients:

Directions:

From The Kitchen Of: ____________________

Notes

Recipe Name

Servings:________ Prep Time:________ Cook Time:________

Ingredients:

Directions:

From The Kitchen Of:

Notes

Recipe Name

Servings:__________ Prep Time:__________ Cook Time:__________

Ingredients:

Directions:

From The Kitchen Of:__________

Notes

Recipe Name

Servings:__________ Prep Time:__________ Cook Time:__________

Ingredients:

Directions:

From The Kitchen Of:

Notes

Recipe Name

Servings:__________ Prep Time:__________ Cook Time:__________

Ingredients:

Directions:

From The Kitchen Of:__________

Notes

Recipe Name

Servings:__________ Prep Time:__________ Cook Time:__________

Ingredients:

Directions:

From The Kitchen Of:__________

Notes

Recipe Name

Servings:__________ Prep Time:__________ Cook Time:__________

Ingredients:

Directions:

From The Kitchen Of:__________

Notes

Recipe Name

Servings:__________ Prep Time:_______________ Cook Time:__________

Ingredients:

Directions:

From The Kitchen Of:____________________

Notes

Recipe Name

Servings:__________ Prep Time:__________ Cook Time:__________

Ingredients:

Directions:

From The Kitchen Of:__________

Notes

Recipe Name

Servings:__________ Prep Time:__________ Cook Time:__________

Ingredients:

Directions:

From The Kitchen Of:__________

Notes

Recipe Name

Servings:__________ Prep Time:__________ Cook Time:__________

Ingredients:

Directions:

From The Kitchen Of:__________

Notes

Recipe Name

Servings:__________ Prep Time:__________ Cook Time:__________

Ingredients:

Directions:

From The Kitchen Of:__________

Notes

Recipe Name

Servings:__________ Prep Time:__________ Cook Time:__________

Ingredients:

Directions:

From The Kitchen Of:__________

Notes

Recipe Name

Servings:__________ Prep Time:______________ Cook Time:__________

Ingredients:

Directions:

From The Kitchen Of:____________________

Notes

Recipe Name

Servings:__________ Prep Time:__________ Cook Time:__________

Ingredients:

Directions:

From The Kitchen Of:__________

Notes

Recipe Name

Servings:__________ Prep Time:______________ Cook Time:__________

Ingredients:

Directions:

From The Kitchen Of:

Notes

Recipe Name

Servings:__________ Prep Time:__________ Cook Time:__________

Ingredients:

Directions:

From The Kitchen Of:

Notes

Recipe Name

Servings:__________ Prep Time:______________ Cook Time:__________

Ingredients:

Directions:

From The Kitchen Of:

Notes

Recipe Name

Servings:__________ Prep Time:__________ Cook Time:__________

Ingredients:

Directions:

From The Kitchen Of:__________

Notes

Recipe Name

Servings:__________ Prep Time:__________ Cook Time:__________

Ingredients:

Directions:

From The Kitchen Of:__________

Notes

Recipe Name

Servings:__________ Prep Time:__________ Cook Time:__________

Ingredients:

Directions:

From The Kitchen Of:__________

Notes

Recipe Name

Servings:__________ Prep Time:_______________ Cook Time:__________

Ingredients:

Directions:

From The Kitchen Of:________________________________

Notes

Recipe Name

Servings:__________ Prep Time:_______________ Cook Time:__________

Ingredients:

Directions:

From The Kitchen Of:____________________

Notes

Recipe Name

Servings:__________ Prep Time:__________ Cook Time:__________

Ingredients:

Directions:

From The Kitchen Of:__________

Notes

Recipe Name

Servings:__________ Prep Time:_______________ Cook Time:__________

Ingredients:

Directions:

From The Kitchen Of:____________________

Notes

Recipe Name

Servings:__________ Prep Time:__________ Cook Time:__________

Ingredients:

Directions:

From The Kitchen Of:__________

Notes

Recipe Name

Servings:__________ Prep Time:__________ Cook Time:__________

Ingredients:

Directions:

From The Kitchen Of:__________

Notes

Recipe Name

Servings:__________ Prep Time:______________ Cook Time:__________

Ingredients:

Directions:

From The Kitchen Of:____________________

Notes

Recipe Name

Servings:__________ Prep Time:__________ Cook Time:__________

Ingredients:

Directions:

From The Kitchen Of:__________

Notes

Recipe Name

Servings:__________ Prep Time:______________ Cook Time:__________

Ingredients:

Directions:

From The Kitchen Of:______________________________

Notes

Recipe Name

Servings:__________ Prep Time:__________ Cook Time:__________

Ingredients:

Directions:

From The Kitchen Of:__________

Notes

Recipe Name

Servings:__________ Prep Time:______________ Cook Time:__________

Ingredients:

Directions:

From The Kitchen Of:

Notes

Recipe Name

Servings:__________ Prep Time:__________ Cook Time:__________

Ingredients:

Directions:

From The Kitchen Of:

Notes

Recipe Name

Servings:__________ Prep Time:______________ Cook Time:__________

Ingredients:

Directions:

From The Kitchen Of:____________________

Notes

Recipe Name

Servings:__________ Prep Time:__________ Cook Time:__________

Ingredients:

Directions:

From The Kitchen Of:

Notes

Recipe Name

Servings:__________ Prep Time:______________ Cook Time:__________

Ingredients:

Directions:

From The Kitchen Of:

Notes

Recipe Name

Servings:__________ Prep Time:______________ Cook Time:__________

Ingredients:

Directions:

From The Kitchen Of:

Notes

Recipe Name

Servings:________ Prep Time:________ Cook Time:________

Ingredients:

Directions:

From The Kitchen Of:

Notes

Recipe Name

Servings:__________ Prep Time:__________ Cook Time:__________

Ingredients:

Directions:

From The Kitchen Of:

Notes

Recipe Name

Servings:__________ Prep Time:______________ Cook Time:__________

Ingredients:

Directions:

From The Kitchen Of:

Notes

Recipe Name

Servings:__________ Prep Time:______________ Cook Time:__________

Ingredients:

Directions:

From The Kitchen Of:

Notes

Recipe Name

Servings:__________ Prep Time:_______________ Cook Time:__________

Ingredients:

Directions:

From The Kitchen Of:____________________

Notes

Recipe Name

Servings:__________ Prep Time:__________ Cook Time:__________

Ingredients:

Directions:

From The Kitchen Of:__________

Notes

Recipe Name

Servings:__________ Prep Time:__________ Cook Time:__________

Ingredients:

Directions:

From The Kitchen Of:

Notes

Recipe Name

Servings:__________ Prep Time:__________ Cook Time:__________

Ingredients:

Directions:

From The Kitchen Of:__________

Notes

Recipe Name

Servings:__________ Prep Time:______________ Cook Time:__________

Ingredients:

Directions:

From The Kitchen Of:______________________________

Notes

Recipe Name

Servings:__________ Prep Time:__________ Cook Time:__________

Ingredients:

Directions:

From The Kitchen Of:__________

Notes

Recipe Name

Servings:__________ Prep Time:__________ Cook Time:__________

Ingredients:

Directions:

From The Kitchen Of:

Notes

Recipe Name

Servings:__________ Prep Time:______________ Cook Time:__________

Ingredients:

Directions:

From The Kitchen Of:____________________

Notes

Recipe Name

Servings:__________ Prep Time:__________ Cook Time:__________

Ingredients:

Directions:

From The Kitchen Of:__________

Notes

Recipe Name

Servings:__________ Prep Time:__________ Cook Time:__________

Ingredients:

Directions:

From The Kitchen Of:

Notes

Recipe Name

Servings:__________ Prep Time:__________ Cook Time:__________

Ingredients:

Directions:

From The Kitchen Of:

Notes

Recipe Name

Servings:__________ Prep Time:______________ Cook Time:__________

Ingredients:

Directions:

From The Kitchen Of:

Notes

Recipe Name

Servings:__________ Prep Time:__________ Cook Time:__________

Ingredients:

Directions:

From The Kitchen Of:

Notes

Recipe Name

Servings:__________ Prep Time:______________ Cook Time:__________

Ingredients:

Directions:

From The Kitchen Of:

Notes

Recipe Name

Servings:__________ Prep Time:______________ Cook Time:__________

Ingredients:

Directions:

From The Kitchen Of:______________________________________

Notes

Recipe Name

Servings:__________ Prep Time:______________ Cook Time:__________

Ingredients:

Directions:

From The Kitchen Of:

Notes

CPSIA information can be obtained
at www.ICGtesting.com
Printed in the USA
LVHW111118121221
705982LV00010B/465

9 781953 557216